COPYRIGHT © 2004 Nanci Bell

Gander Publishing

P.O. Box 780, 450 Front Street

Avila Beach, CA 93424

805-541-5523 • 800-554-1819

VISUALIZING AND VERBALIZING AND V/V ARE REGISTERED TRADEMARKS OF NANCI BELL.

20   19   18   17   10   11   12   13

978-0-945856-34-4

10-171110

Overview and Directions

This workbook is designed to develop gestalt imagery and language comprehension with the *Visualizing and Verbalizing for Language Comprehension and Thinking*® (V/V®) program.

Following the steps of V/V, detail and gestalt imagery are developed with Sentence by Sentence, Multiple Sentence, Whole Paragraph, and Paragraph by Paragraph V/V stimulation.

Each story is high in imagery and followed by these workbook activities:

- Imagery Questions
- Picture Summary
- Word Summary
- Main Idea
- Higher Order Thinking (HOT) Questions
- Paragraph Writing

As the student begins each story, he/she should decode the vocabulary words and visualize the meaning. This will help create imagery and develop contextual fluency. The student may write phrases or partial sentences to describe his/her imagery.

These workbooks have been written specifically to help students learn and discover the wonder of the written word by improving gestalt imagery, critical thinking, and writing skills. Once these skills are developed, the possibilities are endless.

Remember, you can help students do this. You can do anything!

Nanci Bell
2004

There are three workbooks at each reading level:

Book A • Sentence by Sentence
Book B • Sentence by Sentence and Multiple Sentence
Book C • Multiple Sentence, Whole Paragraph, and Paragraph by Paragraph

I am Ivan, King of the Neighborhood. I'm big and wide and full of pride!

I **love** to eat!

I **love** to sleep!

I am a cat!

1

A Shiny New Home

Running across the white sand, the little hermit crab searched for his new home. Soon the crab saw a big shiny shell lying on the sand. He looked inside to make sure the big shell was empty. Then he squeezed out of his small shell and moved into his roomy new one.

Vocabulary:

hermit crab: a small crab
roomy: having lots of space

---

1 **First Sentence:** Running across the white sand, the little hermit crab searched for his new home.

What did those words make you picture? _____

_____

_____

1. What did you picture for the crab? _____

_____

2. What color did you picture the crab? _____

_____

3. How did you picture him running—forward, or side to side? _____

_____

4. Where did you picture him running? _____

_____

---

2 **Second Sentence:** Soon the crab saw a big shiny shell lying on the sand.

What did those words make you picture? _____

_____

_____

1. What did you picture the crab doing? _____

_____

2. What did you see for the crab's eyes? _____

_____

3. Did you picture the shiny shell as bigger or smaller than the crab? ____

_____

4. Did you see the new shell on top of the white sand or buried in the white sand?

_____

Third Sentence: He looked inside to make sure the big shell was empty.

What did those words make you picture? _____

_____

_____

1. What did you picture the crab doing when he went up to the shell?

_____

2. How did you picture him looking inside the shell?_____

_____

3. What did you picture inside the shell?_____

_____

4. Did you picture it dark or light inside the shell?_____

_____

Fourth Sentence: Then he squeezed out of his small shell and moved into his roomy new one.

What did those words make you picture?_____

_____

_____

1. What did you see for the size of the crab's old shell?_____

_____

2. What did you picture for the crab squeezing out of his shell?_____

_____

3. What did you see the crab doing when he moved into the new shell?

_____

4. Did you picture the crab happy or sad in his new home?_____

_____

Picture Summary:

Number your images in order.

____ The crab squeezed into the new shell.

____ The crab saw a big shiny shell lying on the sand.

____ The hermit crab searched for his new home.

____ The crab looked inside the big shell.

Write a Word Summary:

_____

_____

_____

_____

_____

Critical Thinking

Main Idea:

Check the box that best describes all your images—the main idea.

☐ A small crab got inside a big shell.

☐ A small crab found a new shell to live in because its old shell was too small.

☐ A small crab searched the beach for a new shell.

HOT Questions:

1. Why do you think the crab wanted a new shell for his home?_____

_____

2. Why do you think the crab chose this shell for his new home?_____

_____

3. Why do you think the crab made sure the new shell was empty?_____

_____

4. Do you think the crab was more comfortable in his new home? Why or why not?____

_____

5. Do you think the crab will always live in his new shell? Why or why not?_____

_____

6. What do you think happened to the old shell?_____

_____

7. What do you think might be a good title for all this imagery?_____

_____

Make up a story about Harry the Hermit Crab looking for a new home.

_____

_____

_____

_____

_____

_____

_____

_____

_____

_____

_____

_____

_____

_____

_____

_____

Did you use all of the Structure Words? Check each one you used.

| ☐ What | ☐ Size | ☐ Color | ☐ Number | ☐ Shape | ☐ Where |
| ☐ Movement | ☐ Mood | ☐ Background | ☐ Perspective | ☐ When | ☐ Sound |

2 The Flying Snake

The flying snake pressed her long thin body against the tree branch. She wiggled to the very end of the branch and sprang into the air. The snake flattened her body and moved her tail back and forth. She glided through the air and landed safely on another tree.

Vocabulary:

sprang: jumped upward and forward
glided: sailed through the air without effort

---

1 **First Sentence:** The flying snake pressed her long thin body against the tree branch.

What did those words make you picture? _____

_____

_____

1. What did you picture for the snake? _____

_____

2. What color did you picture the snake? _____

_____

3. What did you picture for the tree branch? _____

_____

4. Did you see the snake lying flat on the branch or was she curled around it?

---

2 **Second Sentence:** She wiggled to the very end of the branch and sprang into the air.

What did those words make you picture? _____

_____

_____

1. What did you see for the snake wiggling to get to the end of the branch?

_____

2. Did you picture the snake moving quietly or did she make a rustling sound as she moved?

_____

3. What did you see for the snake springing off the branch? _____

_____

4. What did you picture for the snake in the air? _____

_____

Third Sentence: The snake flattened her body and moved her tail back and forth.

What did those words make you picture? _____

_____

1. What did you picture the snake doing in the air? _____

_____

2. Did you picture the snake moving quickly or slowly through the air?

_____

3. How did you see the snake moving her tail in the air? _____

_____

4. What did you see for the sky as the snake was flying through the air?

_____

Fourth Sentence: She glided through the air and landed safely on another tree.

What did those words make you picture? _____

_____

1. What did you picture for the snake gliding to the other tree? _____

_____

2. Did you picture the trees far apart or close together? _____

_____

3. Did you see the snake being scared or excited as she glided in the air?

_____

4. How did you picture the snake landing safely on the other tree? _____

_____

Picture Summary:

Number your images in order.

_____ The snake landed on another tree.

_____ The snake flattened her body and moved her tail back and forth.

_____ The snake moved to the end of the tree branch and sprang off.

_____ The snake pressed her body against the tree branch.

Write a Word Summary:

_____

_____

_____

_____

_____

Critical Thinking

Main Idea:

Check the box that best describes all your images—the main idea.

☐ A flying snake flattened her body against the tree branch.

☐ There is a flying snake that glides through the air from tree to tree.

☐ A flying snake slithered quietly up the tree.

HOT Questions:

1. Why do you think the snake pressed her body against the branch of the tree and didn't just lie there?_____

_____

2. Why do you think the snake moved to the end of the branch before she jumped?_____

_____

3. Why do you think the snake flattened her body in the air?_____

_____

4. Why do you think it might be important for the snake to move her tail back and forth as she glided?_____

_____

5. Why might the snake travel this way?_____

_____

6. What do you think happened next?_____

_____

7. Why do you think the snake is called a flying snake?_____

_____

Write a Story

Make up a story about Sid the Flying Snake, and what he does on a stormy day.

Did you use all of the Structure Words? Check each one you used.

- ☐ What
- ☐ Movement
- ☐ Size
- ☐ Mood
- ☐ Color
- ☐ Background
- ☐ Number
- ☐ Perspective
- ☐ Shape
- ☐ When
- ☐ Where
- ☐ Sound

8

3 Hummingbird

The hummingbird is a tiny bird with a long curved beak and a colorful body. This little bird moves quickly from flower to flower. Her tiny wings flap so fast they look like a blur. Then she sticks her thin beak into the flowers. Her long tongue helps the bird sip the sweet flower nectar.

Vocabulary:

hummingbird: a small colorful bird that beats its wings so fast they make a humming noise
curved: not straight; rounded; bent
blur: something that is hard to see clearly
beak: the hard part of a bird's mouth
nectar: the juice that is found in a flower

---

1 **First Sentence:** The hummingbird is a tiny bird with a long curved beak and a colorful body.

What did those words make you picture? _____

_____

1. What did you picture for the hummingbird? _____

2. What size did you picture the hummingbird? _____

3. What colors did you see for the hummingbird? _____

4. What did you picture for the hummingbird's beak? _____

---

2 **Second Sentence:** This little bird moves quickly from flower to flower.

What did those words make you picture? _____

_____

1. What did you see for the hummingbird moving quickly? _____

2. What did you see for the flowers? _____

3. How did you see the hummingbird moving from flower to flower?

_____

4. What could you hear in your imagery? _____

Third Sentence: Her tiny wings flap so fast they look like a blur.

What did those words make you picture? _____

_____

_____

1. What did you picture for the hummingbird flapping her wings?_____

_____

2. How did you see them going very fast? _____

_____

3. What did you picture for the hummingbird's wings looking like a blur?

_____

4. Were you picturing this up close or far away? _____

_____

Fifth Sentence: Her long tongue helps the bird sip the sweet flower nectar.

What did those words make you picture? _____

_____

_____

1. What did you picture for the hummingbird's tongue?_____

_____

2. What length did you see for her tongue compared to her tiny body?

_____

3. What did you picture for the flower nectar? _____

_____

Fourth Sentence: Then she sticks her thin beak into the flowers.

What did those words make you picture? _____

_____

_____

1. What did you picture for the hummingbird's beak?_____

_____

2. What color did you see the her beak? _____

_____

3. What size did you see her beak?_____

_____

4. What did you see for the hummingbird sticking her beak into a flower?

_____

Picture Summary:

Number your images in order.

The hummingbird moves from flower to flower.

The hummingbird sticks her thin beak into the flowers.

The hummingbird is a tiny bird with a long curved beak.

The hummingbird's long tongue helps the bird sip the sweet flower nectar.

Critical Thinking

Write a Word Summary:

_____

_____

_____

_____

_____

Main Idea:

Check the box that best describes all your images—the main idea.

☐ The hummingbird has a long tongue to help her sip the sweet flower nectar.

☐ The hummingbird has a curved beak and a colorful body.

☐ The hummingbird is a small bird that flies quickly from flower to flower, stopping to put its long beak in to sip the nectar.

HOT Questions:

1. Why do you think this little bird might be named a _hummingbird_? _____

_____

2. Why do you think the bird might make a humming sound? _____

_____

3. What part of the bird's body makes the sound? _____

_____

4. Why do you think the bird's wings look like a blur when she is flying? _____

_____

5. Why do you think the bird has a long thin beak? _____

_____

6. Why do you think the bird has a long tongue? _____

_____

Write a Story

Make up a story about Hannah the Hummingbird flying to a flower and seeing a cat below.

_____

_____

_____

_____

_____

_____

_____

_____

_____

_____

_____

_____

_____

_____

Did you use all of the Structure Words? Check each one you used.

☐ What　　☐ Size　　☐ Color　　☐ Number　　☐ Shape　　☐ Where

☐ Movement　　☐ Mood　　☐ Background　　☐ Perspective　　☐ When　　☐ Sound

12

4 Penguin Daddy

A small male penguin stands and carefully balances his little white egg on the top of his feet. His soft feathered belly droops down and covers his egg. Keeping his egg warm in the cold Antarctic is hard for the penguin to do by himself. But for three weeks, he works hard to care for his egg. Then the female returns to help raise their chick.

Vocabulary:

penguin: a flightless black and white bird that lives in the very coldest areas
Antarctic: the very cold area around the South Pole

---

1 **First Sentence:** A small male penguin stands and carefully balances his little white egg on the top of his feet.

What did those words make you picture? _____

_____

_____

1. What did you picture for the penguin? _____

_____

2. What color did you picture the egg? _____

_____

3. What did you see for the penguin's feet? _____

_____

4. Where did you see the penguin balancing the egg? _____

_____

2 **Second Sentence:** His soft feathered belly droops down and covers his egg.

What did those words make you picture? _____

_____

_____

1. What did you picture for the penguin's belly? Was it fluffy or smooth?

_____

2. What did you picture for how his belly drooped down? _____

_____

3. Did you see the penguin standing up or lying down as he covered his egg?

_____

4. What did you picture for the ground under the penguin? _____

_____

Third Sentence: Keeping his egg warm in the cold Antarctic is hard for the penguin to do by himself.

What did those words make you picture? _____

_____

_____

1. Did you picture the weather very hot or very cold in the Antarctic?___

_____

2. What did you see it looking like outside if the weather was very cold?

_____

3. Did you see the penguin alone with his egg or were there other penguins around?

_____

4. What did you see for the penguin keeping his egg warm? _____

_____

Fifth Sentence: Then the female returns to help raise their chick.

What did those words make you picture? _____

_____

_____

1. What did you picture for the female penguin returning? _____

_____

2. What did you picture the male penguin doing when he saw her return?

_____

3. What did you picture for the chick? _____

_____

Fourth Sentence: But for three weeks, he works hard to care for his egg.

What did those words make you picture? _____

_____

1. How many weeks did you picture the penguin caring for his egg?___

_____

2. What did you see for the penguin caring for his egg? _____

_____

3. Did you picture the penguin staying with his egg or leaving it?_____

_____

4. What did you see for the penguin working hard? _____

_____

Picture Summary:

Number your images in order.

_____ The male penguin balances his egg on the top of his feet.

_____ The penguin cares for his egg for three weeks.

_____ The female penguin returns to help raise the chick.

_____ The penguin covers his egg with his belly to keep it warm.

14

Critical Thinking

Write a Word Summary:

_____

_____

_____

_____

_____

Main Idea:

Check the box that best describes all your images—the main idea.

☐ The male penguin lives in the cold Antarctic.

☐ The male penguin takes care of his egg in the cold Antarctic on his own for weeks.

☐ The male penguin balances his egg on his feet.

HOT Questions:

1. Why do you think the egg is on the penguin's feet and not on the ground?_____

_____

2. Why do you think it is important for the penguin to have a soft drooping belly?_____

_____

3. Why do you think it is hard to keep the egg warm in the Antarctic?_____

_____

4. What do you think might happen to the egg without the male penguin?_____

_____

5. How might the male penguin prepare to care for his egg for three weeks?_____

_____

6. What do you think the male penguin might do after the female returns? _____

_____

Write a Story

Make up a fun story about Snowball the Penguin.

_____

_____

_____

_____

_____

_____

_____

_____

_____

_____

_____

_____

_____

_____

Did you use all of the Structure Words? Check each one you used.

☐ What ☐ Size ☐ Color ☐ Number ☐ Shape ☐ Where

☐ Movement ☐ Mood ☐ Background ☐ Perspective ☐ When ☐ Sound

5

The Pack Yak

The big hairy brown and white yak walked over the high peaks of Nepal. Huge heavy packs of food and clothing were strapped on his back. Even with the weight, the yak could still walk across the ice and rocks with ease. The cold winds and high mountains didn't stop the yak from carrying supplies for the travelers.

Vocabulary:

yak: a large, long-haired ox that lives in the highlands of Nepal and Tibet
peaks: mountains
Nepal: a country in Central Asia
Tibet: a region in Central Asia that is known for its high mountains

---

1 **First Sentence:** The big hairy brown and white yak walked over the high peaks of Nepal.

What did those words make you picture? _____

_____

_____

1. What did you picture for the yak? _____

_____

2. How did you picture the yak's fur—thick and heavy, or thin and stringy?

_____

3. What size did you picture the yak? _____

_____

4. What did you picture for the high peaks of Nepal? _____

_____

---

2 **Second Sentence:** Huge heavy packs of food and clothing were strapped on his back.

What did those words make you picture? _____

_____

_____

1. What did you picture the yak carrying? _____

_____

2. What colors did you picture for the packs? _____

_____

3. How did you picture the packs being strapped to the yak? _____

_____

4. What did you see the yak doing when the packs were strapped on him?

_____

17

Third Sentence: Even with the weight, the yak could still walk across the ice and rocks with ease.

What did those words make you picture? _____

_____

_____

1. What did you picture for the ice and where did you see it? _____

_____

2. What did you see for the rocks? _____

_____

3. How did you picture the yak walking on the ice and rocks? _____

_____

4. What sounds did you picture as the yak walked with the heavy packs?

_____

Fourth Sentence: The cold winds and high mountains didn't stop the yak from carrying supplies for the travelers.

What did those words make you picture? _____

_____

_____

1. What did you picture for the yak climbing the high mountains in the wind?

_____

2. What might you picture the wind doing to the yak's fur? _____

_____

3. What did you picture for the travelers? _____

_____

4. What sounds could you hear in your imagery? _____

_____

Picture Summary:

Number your images in order.

The yak's fur kept him warm.

The yak climbed over ice and rocks with ease.

The yak had heavy packs on his back.

The yak walked the high peaks of Nepal.

Write a Word Summary:

_____

_____

_____

_____

_____

Critical Thinking

Main Idea:

Check the box that best describes all your images—the main idea.

☐ The yak carries heavy packs through the high mountains for travelers.

☐ The yak lives in a cold region and carries supplies.

☐ Many people travel with yaks across ice and rocks.

HOT Questions:

1. Why might a yak be a good pack animal in the high mountains of Nepal? _____

_____

2. Why do you think it is important for the yak to have long fur? _____

_____

3. Do you think a yak would be useful in the desert? Why or why not? _____

_____

4. Why do you think the yak was able to walk across the ice and rocks with ease? _____

_____

5. Why do you think the cold wind didn't stop the yak? _____

_____

6. Why didn't the travelers carry their packs themselves? _____

_____

7. Why do you think the travelers didn't use cars to cross the mountains of Nepal? _____

_____

Make up a story about climbing a mountain in the snow and wind.

_____

_____

_____

_____

_____

_____

_____

_____

_____

_____

_____

_____

_____

_____

_____

Did you use all of the Structure Words? Check each one you used.

☐ What   ☐ Size   ☐ Color   ☐ Number   ☐ Shape   ☐ Where
☐ Movement   ☐ Mood   ☐ Background   ☐ Perspective   ☐ When   ☐ Sound

6

Riding a Balloon

Two strong men went to the middle of a field and unrolled the red cloth of the hot air balloon. They attached a burner, a fan, and a big basket to the large balloon. As the burner heated the air, the fan blew the hot air into the balloon. The men climbed into the basket and the balloon started to rise. Soon the balloon was floating across the clear blue sky with two happy passengers.

Vocabulary:

burner: a piece of equipment that is lit and creates heat
floating: hanging in the air; not falling

---

1 First Sentence: Two strong men went to the middle of a field and unrolled the red cloth of the hot air balloon.

What did those words make you picture? _____

_____

_____

1. What did you picture for the men? _____

_____

2. What did you picture the men doing? _____

_____

3. What did you picture for the color of the balloon? _____

_____

4. What did you picture for the field? _____

_____

---

2 Second Sentence: They attached a burner, a fan, and a big basket to the large balloon.

What did those words make you picture? _____

_____

_____

1. What did you picture for the basket? _____

_____

2. What did you picture for the men attaching the basket and balloon? ___

_____

3. What did you picture for the burner? _____

_____

4. Did you picture a little fan or a big fan? _____

_____

Third Sentence: As the burner heated the air, the fan blew the hot air into the balloon.

What did those words make you picture? _____

_____

_____

1. What did you picture for the flame from the burner?_____

_____

2. What did you picture for the fan blowing hot air?_____

_____

3. Did you picture a loud roar or were the burner and fans silent?_____

_____

4. What did you see happening to the balloon as the hot air went in it?

_____

Fifth Sentence: Soon the balloon was floating across the clear blue sky with two happy passengers.

What did those words make you picture? _____

_____

_____

1. Did you picture the balloon high in the sky or close to the ground?

_____

2. What did you picture for the sky?_____

_____

3. How did you picture the passengers happy? _____

_____

Fourth Sentence: The men climbed into the basket and the balloon began to rise.

What did those words make you picture? _____

_____

_____

1. What did you picture for the men climbing into the basket?_____

_____

2. Did you picture the men standing or sitting in the basket?_____

_____

3. What did you see happening to the balloon?_____

_____

4. Where did you picture the balloon going?_____

_____

Picture Summary:

Number your images in order.

_____ The balloon floated across the sky.

_____ The balloon was unrolled by two strong men.

_____ The burner made hot air.

_____ The basket was attached to the balloon.

Critical Thinking

Write a Word Summary:

_____

_____

_____

_____

Main Idea:

Check the box that best describes all your images—the main idea.

☐ Two men floated in a hot air balloon.

☐ Two men unrolled the cloth of a balloon not blown up yet.

☐ Two men prepared their hot air balloon and went for a ride.

HOT Questions:

1. Why do you think the hot air balloon is unrolled before it is blown up?_____

_____

2. Why do you think a fan is needed to fill the balloon with air? Why not just blow it up like a regular balloon?_____

_____

3. Why do you think the burner is needed to heat the air?_____

_____

4. Why do you think the balloon has a big basket on it?_____

_____

5. Where do you think hot air balloons got their name?_____

_____

6. How is a hot air balloon different from a regular balloon?_____

_____

Write a Story

Make up a story about taking a trip in a hot air balloon.

_____

_____

_____

_____

_____

_____

_____

_____

_____

_____

_____

_____

_____

_____

Did you use all of the Structure Words? Check each one you used.

☐ What ☐ Size ☐ Color ☐ Number ☐ Shape ☐ Where
☐ Movement ☐ Mood ☐ Background ☐ Perspective ☐ When ☐ Sound

7

The Snake and the Mongoose

The small brown mongoose crept toward the deadly cobra. As the cobra raised its head up to strike, the mongoose quickly darted out of the way. Then, in an instant, the mongoose turned and leapt on the back of the big snake's head. He bit the snake on the head until it was dead.

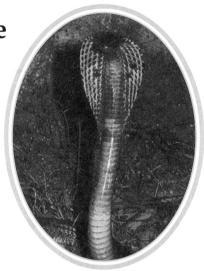

Vocabulary:

mongoose: a small tropical animal with a long body and tail
deadly: able to cause death
cobra: a poisonous snake that can spread out its neck like a hood

1

First Sentence: The small brown mongoose crept toward the deadly cobra.

What did those words make you picture? _____

_____

_____

1. What did you picture for the mongoose? _____

_____

2. What did you picture for the cobra? _____

_____

3. What did you see for the mongoose moving toward the cobra? _____

_____

4. Where did you see all this happening? _____

_____

2

Second Sentence: As the cobra raised its head up to strike, the mongoose quickly darted out of the way.

What did those words make you picture? _____

_____

_____

1. What did you picture for the cobra getting ready to strike? _____

_____

2. What did you picture the mongoose doing? _____

_____

3. How did you see the mongoose darting away? _____

_____

4. Were you picturing this from up close or far away? _____

_____

Third Sentence: Then, in an instant, the mongoose turned and leapt on the back of the big snake's head.

What did those words make you picture? _____

_____

_____

1. What did you picture the mongoose doing now?_____

_____

2. How did you picture the mongoose leaping on the snake? _____

_____

3. How did you picture the mongoose on the snake's head?_____

_____

4. What did you picture the snake doing? _____

_____

Fourth Sentence: He bit the snake on the head until it was dead.

What did those words make you picture? _____

_____

_____

1. What did you picture for the mongoose biting the snake? _____

_____

2. Where did you picture the mongoose biting the snake?_____

_____

3. What did you see for the cobra now?_____

_____

4. What did you picture for the mongoose's mood?_____

_____

Picture Summary:

Number your images in order.

The cobra raised its head to strike.

The mongoose bit the cobra until it was dead.

The mongoose crept up to the cobra.

The mongoose leapt on the snake.

Write a Word Summary:

_____

_____

_____

_____

_____

_____

_____

Main Idea:

Check the box that best describes all your images—the main idea.

☐ The small mongoose killed the deadly cobra by biting it on the head.

☐ The small mongoose jumped on the deadly cobra.

☐ The cobra tried to strike the mongoose and kill it.

HOT Questions:

1. Why do you think the mongoose crept toward the cobra instead of running away? _____

2. Why do you think the cobra didn't ignore the mongoose or move away? _____

3. Why do you think the cobra lifted its head off the ground? _____

4. Why do you think the mongoose darted out of the cobra's way? _____

5. Why do you think the mongoose turned and leapt on the snake? _____

6. Why do you think the mongoose leapt on the back of the snake's head? _____

7. Do you think the mongoose is slow or quick? Why? _____

Write a Story

Make up a story about Mel the Mongoose going on a walk and suddenly seeing a cobra.

_____

_____

_____

_____

_____

_____

_____

_____

_____

_____

_____

_____

_____

_____

_____

Did you use all of the Structure Words? Check each one you used.

- ☐ What
- ☐ Movement
- ☐ Size
- ☐ Mood
- ☐ Color
- ☐ Background
- ☐ Number
- ☐ Perspective
- ☐ Shape
- ☐ When
- ☐ Where
- ☐ Sound

8

Digging for Diamonds

Ann set out her small shovel on the soft brown dirt at Diamond Crater State Park. She dug a small hole and placed each scoop of dirt into a box that had a screen at the bottom. Ann shook the box gently. The sifted dirt fell through the screen leaving a shiny stone in one corner. Ann had found a real diamond!

Vocabulary:

diamond: a type of gem or stone that is very hard and very valuable
screen: a wire net
sifted: shook a screen so that small pieces go through and large ones stay behind

---

1 **First Sentence:** Ann set out her small shovel on the soft brown dirt at Diamond Crater State Park.

What did those words make you picture? _____

_____

_____

1. What did you picture for Ann? _____

_____

2. What color did you picture the dirt at the park? _____

_____

3. What did you picture for the small shovel? _____

_____

4. What did you see for the park? _____

_____

---

2 **Second Sentence:** She dug a small hole and placed each scoop of dirt into a box that had a screen at the bottom.

What did those words make you picture? _____

_____

_____

1. What did you picture for Ann digging the hole? _____

_____

2. What did you picture for the hole? _____

_____

3. What did you picture for the box? _____

_____

4. What did you picture for the screen? _____

_____

Third Sentence: Ann shook the box gently.

What did those words make you picture? _____

_____

1. What did you picture for Ann shaking the box? _____

_____

2. How did you picture Ann shaking the box *gently*? _____

_____

3. What sounds did you picture? _____

_____

4. Did you picture this up close or from far away? _____

_____

Fourth Sentence: The sifted dirt fell through the screen leaving a shiny stone in one corner.

What did those words make you picture? _____

_____

1. What did you picture for the sifted dirt? _____

_____

2. How many stones did you see in the bottom of the box? _____

_____

3. What size did you picture for the stone? _____

_____

4. What color did you picture the stone? _____

_____

Fifth Sentence: Ann had found a real diamond!

What did those words make you picture? _____

_____

1. What did you picture for the diamond? _____

_____

2. What shape did you picture the diamond? _____

_____

3. What mood did you picture for Ann? _____

_____

Picture Summary:

Number your images in order.

Ann shook the box gently.

Ann dug a hole in the dirt.

Ann had found a real diamond.

Ann put the dirt into a box.

Critical Thinking

Write a Word Summary:

_____

_____

_____

_____

Main Idea:

Check the box that best describes all your images—the main idea.

☐ Ann went to the park and dug in the dirt.

☐ Ann sifted through the dirt at the park and found a diamond.

☐ Ann sifted dirt through a box with a screen on the bottom.

HOT Questions:

1. Why do you think the park is named Diamond Crater?_____

_____

2. Why do you think Ann needed a shovel for the park?_____

_____

3. Why do you think Ann dug a hole in the ground?_____

_____

4. Why do you think Ann had a box with a screen in the bottom?_____

_____

5. Why do you think Ann shook the box after she put the dirt in it?_____

_____

6. Do you think Ann was surprised when she found a diamond? Why or why not?_____

_____

Make up a story about finding treasure.

_____

_____

_____

_____

_____

_____

_____

_____

_____

_____

_____

_____

_____

Did you use all of the Structure Words? Check each one you used.

☐ What ☐ Size ☐ Color ☐ Number ☐ Shape ☐ Where
☐ Movement ☐ Mood ☐ Background ☐ Perspective ☐ When ☐ Sound

9

The Great Find

Sue Hendrickson was walking in a dusty valley looking for fossils. Suddenly, she looked up and saw some large white bones in a sandy cliff above her. She climbed up the cliff and saw five huge bones sticking out of the ground. She yelled, "Dinosaur bones!" and ran as fast as she could back to camp.

Vocabulary:

fossil: the hardened remains of a plant or animal from an earlier age
dinosaur: a type of large reptile that lived millions of years ago

---

1 **First Sentence:** Sue Hendrickson was walking in a dusty valley looking for fossils.

What did those words make you picture? _____

_____

_____

1. What did you picture for Sue? _____

_____

2. What did you picture Sue wearing? _____

_____

3. How did you see Sue looking for fossils? _____

_____

4. What did you picture for the valley? _____

_____

2 **Second Sentence:** Suddenly, she looked up and saw some large white bones in a sandy cliff above her.

What did those words make you picture? _____

_____

_____

1. What did you picture Sue doing? _____

_____

2. What did you picture for Sue seeing the bones? _____

_____

3. What did you see for the bones? _____

_____

4. What did you picture for the cliff? _____

_____

Third Sentence: She climbed up the cliff and saw five huge bones sticking out of the ground.

What did those words make you picture? _____

_____

1. What did you see for Sue climbing up the cliff?_____

_____

2. What did you picture for the bones now?_____

_____

3. What did you picture for the bones sticking out of the ground?_____

_____

4. Where did you picture all this happening?_____

_____

Fourth Sentence: She yelled, "Dinosaur bones!" and ran as fast as she could back to camp.

What did those words make you picture? _____

_____

1. What did you picture for Sue yelling?_____

_____

2. What did you picture for the dinosaur bones?_____

_____

3. What did you see for Sue running back to camp?_____

_____

4. What did you picture for Sue's camp? _____

_____

Picture Summary:

Number your images in order.

_____ Sue saw some large white bones.

_____ Sue ran back to camp.

_____ Sue was walking in a valley.

_____ Sue climbed up a cliff.

Write a Word Summary:

_____

_____

_____

_____

_____

_____

Critical Thinking

Main Idea:

Check the box that best describes all your images—the main idea.

☐ Sue climbed on some rocky cliffs.   ☐ Sue ran back to her camp.   ☐ Sue found some dinosaur bones in a cliff.

HOT Questions:

1. Why do you think Sue was in the valley? _____

_____

2. Why do you think Sue decided to take a closer look at the large white bones sticking out of the cliff? _____

_____

3. Why do you think the bones were sticking out of the cliff and not laying on the ground? _____

_____

4. How do you think Sue knew they were dinosaur bones? _____

_____

5. Why do you think Sue yelled and ran quickly to tell the others in her camp? _____

_____

6. Why do you think it would be exciting for Sue to find dinosaur bones? _____

_____

7. What do you think happened next? _____

_____

Make up a story about living with dinosaurs.

_____

_____

_____

_____

_____

_____

_____

_____

_____

_____

_____

_____

_____

_____

_____

_____

_____

_____

Did you use all of the Structure Words? Check each one you used.

- ☐ What
- ☐ Movement
- ☐ Size
- ☐ Mood
- ☐ Color
- ☐ Background
- ☐ Number
- ☐ Perspective
- ☐ Shape
- ☐ When
- ☐ Where
- ☐ Sound

10

Lunchtime for Venus

A tiny black fly landed on a small green plant. As the fly explored the surface of the plant, it touched some short plant hairs on the leaves. Suddenly, the leaves snapped together trapping the fly. It was lunchtime for the Venus flytrap!

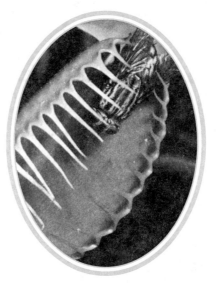

Vocabulary:

explored: traveled around
surface: the top part
Venus flytrap: a plant that eats insects

---

1 **First Sentence:** A tiny black fly landed on a small green plant.

What did those words make you picture? _____

_____

_____

1. What size and color did you picture the fly? _____

_____

2. What did you picture for the plant? _____

_____

3. What color did you picture the plant? _____

_____

4. Did you picture the fly landing gently on the plant or crashing into it?

_____

---

2 **Second Sentence:** As the fly explored the surface of the plant, it touched some short plant hairs on the leaves.

What did those words make you picture? _____

_____

_____

1. What did you picture for the fly exploring the plant?_____

_____

2. How big did you picture the plant hairs on the leaves?_____

_____

3. Did you picture the fly touching the plant hairs with its wings or with its legs?

_____

4. Were you picturing the fly up close or far away?_____

Third Sentence: Suddenly, the leaves snapped together trapping the fly.

What did those words make you picture? _____

_____

1. What did you picture for the size of the green leaves that snapped together?
   _____

2. How did you picture the leaves snapping together? _____

   _____

3. How did you picture the fly being trapped? _____

   _____

4. What sounds could you hear? _____

   _____

Fourth Sentence: It was lunchtime for the Venus flytrap!

What did those words make you picture? _____

_____

1. What did you picture for "lunchtime"? _____

   _____

2. How did you picture the plant eating? _____

   _____

3. What did you picture the plant doing when it had finished eating? ___

   _____

4. Were you picturing all this up close or far away? _____

   _____

Picture Summary:

Number your images in order.

[ ] The fly touched some plant hairs on the leaves as it explored.

[ ] The fly landed on a small green plant.

[ ] The plant ate lunch.

[ ] The leaves snapped shut.

Write a Word Summary:

_____

_____

_____

_____

_____

_____

_____

Critical Thinking

Main Idea:

Check the box that best describes all your images—the main idea.

☐ A small black fly ate a plant called a Venus flytrap.

☐ A small black fly was eaten by a Venus flytrap.

☐ A Venus flytrap had lunch.

HOT Questions:

1. Why do you think the fly landed on the plant?_____

_____

2. Why do you think the fly explored the surface of the plant?_____

_____

3. Why do you think the plant had short hairs on its leaves?_____

_____

4. How do you think the leaves knew to snap together on the fly?_____

_____

5. Why do you think the leaves snapped together on the fly?_____

_____

6. What do you think happened next?_____

_____

7. How do you think this plant is different from most plants?_____

_____

Make up a story about an adventure you went on for lunch.

_____

_____

_____

_____

_____

_____

_____

_____

_____

_____

_____

_____

_____

_____

Did you use all of the Structure Words? Check each one you used.

| ☐ What | ☐ Size | ☐ Color | ☐ Number | ☐ Shape | ☐ Where |
| ☐ Movement | ☐ Mood | ☐ Background | ☐ Perspective | ☐ When | ☐ Sound |

11

Carter's Find

In Egypt in 1922, Howard Carter walked down the stone steps and stood before the door to the tomb. A warm rush of stale air came through the open door. Then Carter lit a candle and peered inside. In the flickering light, Carter saw stone vases, statues, and a huge golden throne. He had found the rich tomb of the young Egyptian King Tut.

Vocabulary:

tomb: a place where a person is buried
rush: a quick movement
stale: not fresh; old
peered: looked carefully
flickering: not steady; fading and getting stronger
throne: a chair that is used by a king or queen

---

1 **First Sentence:** In Egypt in 1922, Howard Carter walked down the stone steps and stood before the door to the tomb.

What did those words make you picture? _____

_____

1. What did you picture for Howard Carter? _____

2. What did you picture for the tomb? _____

3. What did you picture for the steps? _____

4. What did you see for the door—wooden, stone, or...? _____

---

2 **Second Sentence:** A warm rush of stale air came through the open door.

What did those words make you picture? _____

_____

1. What did you picture for the air rushing through the door? _____

2. Did you picture a light breeze or a large gust of wind? _____

3. What did you picture for the open door? _____

4. What did you see for Carter as the air rushed through the open door?

_____

Third Sentence: Then Carter lit a candle and peered inside.

What did those words make you picture? _____

_____

1. What did you picture for the candle? _____

_____

2. How did you picture Carter lighting a candle? _____

_____

3. What did you see for Carter peering inside the tomb? _____

_____

4. What mood did you picture for Carter as he looked inside? _____

Fifth Sentence: He had found the rich tomb of the young Egyptian King Tut.

What did those words make you picture? _____

_____

1. What did you picture for the rich tomb?

_____

2. What mood did you picture Carter being in when he realized it was the tomb of a rich king?

_____

3. Did you picture this up close or far away? _____

_____

Fourth Sentence: In the flickering light, Carter saw stone vases, statues, and a huge golden throne.

What did those words make you picture? _____

_____

1. What did you picture for the flickering light? _____

_____

2. What did you picture Carter seeing inside the tomb? _____

_____

3. What did you see for the vases and the statues? _____

_____

4. What did you see for the throne? _____

_____

Picture Summary:

Number your images in order.

_____ Carter had found King Tut's rich tomb.

_____ Carter climbed down the stone stairs to the open door.

_____ Carter felt a rush of stale air.

_____ Carter peered inside the tomb, holding a candle for light.

Critical Thinking

Write a Word Summary:

_____

_____

_____

_____

_____

Main Idea:

Check the box that best describes all your images—the main idea.

☐ Howard Carter found many treasures in a tomb.

☐ Howard Carter went through an open door in a tomb in Egypt.

☐ Howard Carter found the rich tomb of King Tut.

HOT Questions:

1. Why do you think Carter wanted to enter the tomb?_____

_____

2. Why do you think the air that came out of the tomb was stale and warm?_____

_____

3. Why do you think Carter used a candle to see inside the tomb and didn't just turn on the lights?_____

_____

4. Why do you think the light was flickering?_____

_____

5. Why do you think there was a golden throne in the tomb?_____

_____

6. Do you think anyone had been in the tomb before Carter? Why or why not?_____

_____

Make up a story about your life if you were a king.

_____

_____

_____

_____

_____

_____

_____

_____

_____

_____

_____

_____

_____

Did you use all of the Structure Words? Check each one you used.

| ☐ What | ☐ Size | ☐ Color | ☐ Number | ☐ Shape | ☐ Where |
| ☐ Movement | ☐ Mood | ☐ Background | ☐ Perspective | ☐ When | ☐ Sound |

12

Shearing the Sheep

The woolly white sheep was led into the old red barn. The farmer held her tightly so she would not move while she was being sheared. Then he ran electric clippers down the sheep, cutting off all the heavy wool without hurting her. In a few moments, the thick wool had been cut off and the sheep was set free.

Vocabulary:

clippers: tool used to cut or shear hair
wool: the hair of a sheep
sheared: cut off wool or hair

---

1 First Sentence: The woolly white sheep was led into the old red barn.

What did those words make you picture? _____

_____

_____

1. What did you picture for the sheep? _____

_____

2. What did you see for the wool on the sheep? _____

_____

3. What did you picture for the barn? _____

_____

4. How did you picture the sheep being led into the barn? _____

_____

---

2 Second Sentence: The farmer held her tightly so she would not move while she was being sheared.

What did those words make you picture? _____

_____

_____

1. What did you picture for the farmer? _____

_____

2. How did you picture the farmer holding the sheep—by the feet, around the middle, or...?

_____

3. Did you picture the sheep standing up or lying down while she was being sheared?

_____

4. Did you picture the sheep sitting quietly or struggling to get loose?

_____

Third Sentence: Then he ran electric clippers down the sheep, cutting off all the heavy wool without hurting her.

What did those words make you picture? _____

_____

1. What did you picture for electric clippers?_____

_____

2. What did you see for the clippers cutting off the wool?_____

_____

3. What sound did you picture for the electric clippers? _____

_____

4. What did you picture for the mood of the sheep?_____

_____

Fourth Sentence: In a few moments, the thick wool had been cut off and the sheep was set free.

What did those words make you picture? _____

_____

1. What did you picture for the wool being cut off?_____

_____

2. What did you picture for the sheep now?_____

_____

3. Did you picture the sheared wool in one big piece or many smaller pieces?

_____

4. What did you see the sheep doing when she was set free? _____

_____

Picture Summary:

Number your images in order.

_____ The sheep was set free.

_____ The farmer ran the clippers down the sheep.

_____ The white sheep was led into the red barn.

_____ The farmer held the sheep tightly.

Write a Word Summary:

_____

_____

_____

_____

_____

_____

Critical Thinking

Main Idea:

Check the box that best describes all your images—the main idea.

☐ The farmer led a white sheep into the barn.

☐ The farmer sheared the white wool off the sheep and set her free.

☐ The farmer sheared the sheep with electric clippers.

HOT Questions:

1. Why do you think the sheep was led into the barn? _____

_____

2. Why do you think the sheep was sheared inside a barn and not outside?_____

_____

3. Why do you think it was important that the sheep not be able to move?_____

_____

4. Why do you think the farmer used electric clippers instead of scissors?_____

_____

5. Why do you think it took only a few moments for the farmer to shear the sheep?___

_____

6. Do you think it is important to shear the sheep? Why or why not?_____

_____

7. What do you think might have happened to a sheep if the wool wasn't cut off?_____

Make up a story about being on a farm when it is time to shear the sheep.

_____

_____

_____

_____

_____

_____

_____

_____

_____

_____

_____

_____

_____

_____

Did you use all of the Structure Words? Check each one you used.

☐ What	☐ Size	☐ Color	☐ Number	☐ Shape	☐ Where
☐ Movement	☐ Mood	☐ Background	☐ Perspective	☐ When	☐ Sound

13

A Crunchy Lunch

The small brown hedgehog waddled over the soft dirt. With her long snout, she could smell bugs hidden in the dirt. Soon, the hedgehog had a meal of nice crunchy bugs. Then she rolled herself into a tight ball and fell asleep. Her spiny quills protected her from harm during her nap.

Vocabulary:

waddled: walked with short, swaying steps
snout: the nose and mouth of an animal
quill: a needle-like object

1 **First Sentence:** The small brown hedgehog waddled over the soft dirt.

What did those words make you picture? _____

_____

1. What did you picture for the hedgehog? _____

2. What did you picture for the hedgehog waddling? _____

3. Where did you picture her—in a forest, down a sidewalk, or...? _____

4. What did you picture for the soft dirt? _____

2 **Second Sentence:** With her long snout, she could smell bugs hidden in the dirt.

What did those words make you picture? _____

_____

1. What did you picture for the hedgehog's snout? _____

2. What did you see for the hedgehog smelling the dirt? _____

3. What did you see the hedgehog doing with her nose? _____

4. What did you picture for the bugs? _____

Third Sentence: Soon, the hedgehog had a meal of nice crunchy bugs.

What did those words make you picture? _____

_____

_____

1. What did you picture for *crunchy* bugs? _____

_____

2. How did you picture the hedgehog eating the bugs? _____

_____

3. How many bugs did you picture the hedgehog eating? _____

_____

4. What sounds could you hear in this imagery? _____

_____

Fourth Sentence: Then she rolled herself into a tight ball and fell asleep.

What did those words make you picture? _____

_____

_____

1. What did you picture for the hedgehog rolling? _____

_____

2. What did you picture for the hedgehog in a ball? _____

_____

3. What did you picture for the hedgehog sleeping? _____

_____

4. How were you picturing this, up close or from far away? _____

_____

Fifth Sentence: Her spiny quills protected her from harm during her nap.

What did those words make you picture? _____

_____

_____

1. What did you see for the spiny quills? _____

_____

2. How many quills did you picture on the hedgehog? _____

_____

3. What did you see for the hedgehog taking a nap? _____

_____

Picture Summary:

Number your images in order.

The hedgehog took a nap.

The hedgehog smelled for bugs.

The hedgehog rolled into a ball.

The hedgehog ate some bugs.

Critical Thinking

Write a Word Summary:

_____

_____

_____

_____

Main Idea:

Check the box that best describes all your images—the main idea.

☐ The brown hedgehog took a nap after eating some bugs.

☐ The brown hedgehog waddled back and forth on the soft dirt.

☐ The brown hedgehog ate crunchy bugs.

HOT Questions:

1. Why do you think the hedgehog needs a long snout?_____

_____

2. How do you think the hedgehog finds the bugs for her meal?_____

_____

3. Why might it be important for a hedgehog to look for bugs in soft dirt?_____

_____

4. How do you think the spiny quills protect the hedgehog? _____

_____

5. Why do you think the hedgehog rolled herself into a tight ball before sleeping? _____

_____

6. What do you think might happen to the hedgehog if she lay flat on her back to sleep? ___

_____

Make up a story about Hazel the Hedgehog looking for bugs one day and a wolf came along.

_____

_____

_____

_____

_____

_____

_____

_____

_____

_____

_____

_____

_____

Did you use all of the Structure Words? Check each one you used.

- ☐ What
- ☐ Movement
- ☐ Size
- ☐ Mood
- ☐ Color
- ☐ Background
- ☐ Number
- ☐ Perspective
- ☐ Shape
- ☐ When
- ☐ Where
- ☐ Sound

14

Reggie's Long Walk

When Reggie Miller, the basketball player, was small, he had to wear braces on his legs. The braces were heavy, so Reggie sat while the other kids played. When he was five, the doctors removed his leg braces. Reggie began to walk and then run. Soon he was playing basketball and on his way to becoming a professional basketball star.

Vocabulary:

braces: devices used to strengthen a part of the body

---

1 First Sentence: When Reggie Miller, the basketball player, was small, he had to wear braces on his legs.

What did those words make you picture? _____

_____

1. What did you picture for Reggie Miller? _____

2. What did you picture for a basketball player? _____

3. What did you picture for Reggie when he was small? _____

4. What did you see Reggie wearing on his legs? _____

---

2 Second Sentence: The braces were heavy, so Reggie sat while the other kids played.

What did those words make you picture? _____

_____

1. What did you picture to show that the braces were heavy? _____

2. Did you picture Reggie sitting by himself or with other kids? _____

3. What did you picture Reggie doing as he sat? _____

4. What did you see the other kids doing? _____

Third Sentence: When he was five, the doctors removed his leg braces.

What did those words make you picture? _____

_____

1. What did you picture to show Reggie was five? _____

   _____

2. What did you picture for the doctors? _____

   _____

3. What did you picture the doctors doing? _____

   _____

4. What mood did you picture Reggie in when the braces were removed?

   _____

Fourth Sentence: Reggie began to walk and then run.

What did those words make you picture? _____

_____

1. What did you picture for Reggie beginning to walk? _____

   _____

2. Did you picture Reggie walking easily at first or was it difficult? _____

   _____

3. What did you picture for Reggie running? _____

   _____

4. What mood did you see for Reggie when he first walked? _____

   _____

Fifth Sentence: Soon he was playing basketball and on his way to becoming a professional basketball star.

What did those words make you picture? _____

_____

1. What did you picture Reggie playing? _____

   _____

2. What did you picture for Reggie as a professional player? _____

   _____

3. How did you picture Reggie as a star? _____

   _____

Picture Summary:

Number these in order.

_____ Reggie went on to become a basketball star.

_____ Reggie Miller wore braces on his legs when he was small.

_____ The doctors removed the braces when Reggie was five.

_____ Reggie watched the other kids playing as he sat.

Critical Thinking

Write a Word Summary:

_____

_____

_____

_____

_____

Main Idea:

Check the box that best describes all your images—the main idea.

☐ Reggie wore braces on his legs until he was five.

☐ Reggie became a star basketball player.

☐ Even though he wore leg braces until he was five, Reggie became a basketball star.

HOT Questions:

1. Why do you think Reggie could not run or play when he was small? _____

_____

2. Why do you think the braces made it difficult for Reggie to run and play? _____

_____

3. Why do you think Reggie had to sit and watch the other kids play? _____

_____

4. Why do you think Reggie began to walk before he ran? _____

_____

5. Do you think it was hard for Reggie to learn to walk and run? Why or why not? _____

_____

6. Why do you think Reggie was able to become a star basketball player? _____

_____

Write a Story

Make up a story about anything you want!

_____

_____

_____

_____

_____

_____

_____

_____

_____

_____

_____

_____

_____

_____

_____

_____

_____

Did you use all of the Structure Words? Check each one you used.

- ☐ What
- ☐ Movement
- ☐ Size
- ☐ Mood
- ☐ Color
- ☐ Background
- ☐ Number
- ☐ Perspective
- ☐ Shape
- ☐ When
- ☐ Where
- ☐ Sound

15 Handy Sandwich

John Montague, the Earl of Sandwich, sat at the table and felt his stomach grumble. He had been playing cards with his friends for hours. Hungry, he called for a waiter to bring him meat and cheese between two slices of bread. Now he could eat and play cards without getting the cards greasy. Soon the Earl's friends asked to have "the same as Sandwich," and that's where we got the name!

Vocabulary:

Earl: a royal title, like King or Queen
grumble: growl; make noise
greasy: covered with oil

---

1 **First Sentence:** John Montague, the Earl of Sandwich, sat at the table and felt his stomach grumble.

What did those words make you picture? _____

_____

1. What did you picture for the Earl? _____

_____

2. What did you see the Earl doing? _____

_____

3. What did you picture for the table? _____

_____

4. What sound did you picture for the Earl's stomach grumbling? _____

_____

---

2 **Second Sentence:** He had been playing cards with his friends for hours.

What did those words make you picture? _____

_____

1. What did you see for the Earl playing cards? _____

_____

2. What did you picture for the cards? _____

_____

3. How many people did you picture the Earl playing cards with? _____

_____

4. What mood did you picture for the Earl and his friends? _____

_____

Third Sentence: Hungry, he called for a waiter to bring him meat and cheese between two slices of bread.

What did those words make you picture? _____

_____

1. What did you see for the Earl calling a waiter? _____

_____

2. What did you picture for the waiter? _____

_____

3. What did you picture for the bread? _____

_____

4. What did you picture for the meat and cheese? _____

_____

Fifth Sentence: Soon the Earl's friends asked to have "the same as Sandwich," and that's where we got the name!

What did those words make you picture? _____

_____

1. What did you picture for the Earl's friends? _____

_____

2. What did you picture the friends doing? _____

_____

3. What did you picture for "sandwich"? _____

_____

Fourth Sentence: Now he could eat and play cards without getting the cards greasy.

What did those words make you picture? _____

_____

1. What did you picture the Earl eating? _____

_____

2. Did you picture the Earl using one hand or two to eat? _____

_____

3. What did you see the Earl doing while he was eating? _____

_____

4. What did you picture for the cards while the Earl was eating? _____

_____

Picture Summary:

Number your images in order.

The Earl's friends asked the waiter to bring them "the same as Sandwich."

The Earl had been playing cards for hours and his stomach grumbled.

The Earl asked the waiter to bring him meat and cheese between two slices of bread.

Now the Earl could eat and play cards at the same time.

Critical Thinking

Write a Word Summary:

_____

_____

_____

_____

Main Idea:

Check the box that best describes all your images—the main idea.

☐ John Montague invented the sandwich so he could eat and play cards at the same time.

☐ John Montague had meat and cheese between two slices of bread.

☐ John Montague ate a sandwich so his cards wouldn't get greasy.

HOT Questions:

1. Why do you think the Earl's stomach began to grumble?_____

_____

2. Why do you think the Earl did not stop playing cards long enough to eat?_____

_____

3. Why do you think the Earl ordered meat and cheese to be put between slices of bread?_____

_____

4. Why do you think it was important not to get the cards greasy?_____

_____

5. Why would putting food between slices of bread stop the cards from getting greasy? _____

_____

6. Why do you think this food became known as the sandwich?_____

_____

Write a Story

Make up a story about anything you want!

_____

_____

_____

_____

_____

_____

_____

_____

_____

_____

_____

_____

_____

_____

_____

Did you use all of the Structure Words? Check each one you used.

☐ What   ☐ Size   ☐ Color   ☐ Number   ☐ Shape   ☐ Where
☐ Movement   ☐ Mood   ☐ Background   ☐ Perspective   ☐ When   ☐ Sound

16

The Tower of Pisa

The Leaning Tower of Pisa is one of the most loved sites in Italy. But for many years, the tower was close to falling over. So workers took some soil from under one side of the tower. Inch by inch, the tower moved a little straighter. The tower still leans, but it is now safe for people to visit.

Vocabulary:

Italy: a country in Southern Europe
soil: dirt

---

1 **First Sentence:** The Leaning Tower of Pisa is one of the most loved sites in Italy.

What did those words make you picture? _____

_____

_____

1. What did you picture for the Tower of Pisa? _____

2. What color did you picture for the tower? _____

3. What did you picture for Italy? _____

4. What did you see for the tower being loved? _____

---

2 **Second Sentence:** But for many years, the tower was close to falling over.

What did those words make you picture? _____

_____

_____

1. What did you picture for the tower being close to falling over? _____

2. How close did you see the tower leaning to the ground? _____

3. How did you picture it being "many years"? _____

4. Were you seeing the tower up close or from far away? _____

Third Sentence: So workers took some soil from under one side of the tower.

What did those words make you picture? _____

_____

1. What did you picture for the workers? _____

_____

2. What did you see for the workers removing soil? _____

_____

3. Did you picture them taking the soil from next to the tower or under the tower?

_____

4. Did you picture them removing a little soil or a lot of soil? _____

_____

Fourth Sentence: Inch by inch, the tower moved a little straighter.

What did those words make you picture? _____

_____

1. What did you picture for the tower moving "inch by inch"? _____

_____

2. How fast did you picture the tower moving? _____

_____

3. What did you see for the tower moving straighter? _____

_____

4. What sounds could you hear? _____

_____

Fifth Sentence: The tower still leans, but it is now safe for people to visit.

What did those words make you picture? _____

_____

1. How did you see the tower leaning now? _____

_____

2. What did you picture for the tower being safe? _____

_____

3. What did you picture for people visiting the tower? _____

_____

Picture Summary:

Number your images in order.

The Tower of Pisa in Italy was falling over.

The tower still leans, but it won't fall over.

Workers took soil from under one side of the tower.

Inch by inch, the tower moved a little straighter.

Critical Thinking

Write a Word Summary:

_____

_____

_____

_____

Main Idea:

Check the box that best describes all your images—the main idea.

☐ Each year, the Tower of Pisa leaned further toward the ground.

☐ Workers moved soil from under the Tower of Pisa.

☐ Workers stopped the Tower of Pisa from falling over by removing dirt from under one side.

HOT Questions:

1. Why do you think the tower is named the "Leaning Tower" of Pisa? _____

_____

2. Why do you think the tower is one of the most loved sites in Italy? _____

_____

3. Why do you think the workers tried to straighten the tower? _____

_____

4. Why do you think soil was removed from under one side of the tower and not from under the whole tower? _____

_____

5. Do you think the workers wanted to fix the tower so that it will be straight? Why or why not? _____

_____

6. Do you think the tower will ever fall over? Why or why not? _____

_____

Make up a story about visiting the Leaning Tower of Pisa.

_____
_____
_____
_____
_____
_____
_____
_____
_____
_____
_____
_____
_____
_____
_____
_____
_____

Did you use all of the Structure Words? Check each one you used.

- ☐ What
- ☐ Size
- ☐ Color
- ☐ Number
- ☐ Shape
- ☐ Where
- ☐ Movement
- ☐ Mood
- ☐ Background
- ☐ Perspective
- ☐ When
- ☐ Sound

17

A Reindeer Sled Ride

Jon ran in the snow wearing his warmest clothes and boots. The cold Arctic air blew as he caught his pet reindeer. Quickly, he harnessed the reindeer to his bright red sled. Then off they went over the hills of snowy northern Finland.

Vocabulary:

Arctic: the very cold area around the North Pole
Finland: a country in Northern Europe
harnessed: placed a set of straps on an animal that are often attached to a sled or wagon

---

1 **First Sentence:** Jon ran in the snow wearing his warmest clothes and boots.

What did those words make you picture? _____

_____

_____

1. What did you picture for Jon? _____

_____

2. What did you picture for Jon's clothes and boots? _____

_____

3. How did you picture Jon moving? _____

_____

4. Where did you see Jon running? _____

_____

---

2 **Second Sentence:** The cold Arctic air blew as he caught his pet reindeer.

What did those words make you picture? _____

_____

_____

1. What did you picture for cold Arctic air? _____

_____

2. What did you picture for the wind blowing? _____

_____

3. What did you see for the pet reindeer? _____

_____

4. How did you see Jon catching the reindeer? _____

_____

Third Sentence: Quickly, he harnessed the reindeer to his bright red sled.

What did those words make you picture? _____

_____

_____

1. What did you picture for the harness? _____

_____

2. What did you picture for Jon harnessing his reindeer?_____

_____

3. What did you picture for the sled? _____

_____

4. Where did you see the reindeer, at the front of the sled or in the back?

_____

Fourth Sentence: Then off they went over the hills of snowy northern Finland.

What did those words make you picture? _____

_____

_____

1. What did you picture Jon and the reindeer doing now?_____

_____

2. Did you picture the sled gliding smoothly over the snowy hills or was it a bumpy ride?

_____

3. What did you picture for the sound of the sled on the snow? _____

_____

4. What did you see for the countryside?_____

_____

Picture Summary:

Number your images in order.

_____ They rode off over the snowy hills.

_____ Jon caught his pet reindeer.

_____ Jon ran outside in his warmest clothes.

_____ Jon harnessed the reindeer to his sled.

Write a Word Summary:

_____

_____

_____

_____

_____

Critical Thinking

Main Idea:

Check the box that best describes all your images—the main idea.

☐ Jon harnessed his pet reindeer and went for a ride on his sled.

☐ Jon caught his pet reindeer.

☐ Jon went for a ride in Northern Finland.

HOT Questions:

1. Why do you think Jon needed to wear his warmest clothes and boots?_____

_____

2. Why do you think Jon had a pet reindeer?_____

_____

3. Why might it be a good idea to harness the reindeer quickly?_____

_____

4. Why do you think Jon used a sled and not a car to travel in northern Finland?_____

_____

5. Why do you think a reindeer might be a good animal to pull a sled?_____

_____

6. What do you think happened next?_____

_____

7. What might be another title for these images?_____

_____

Make up a story about a reindeer.

_____

_____

_____

_____

_____

_____

_____

_____

_____

_____

_____

_____

_____

_____

_____

_____

Did you use all of the Structure Words? Check each one you used.

☐ What	☐ Size	☐ Color	☐ Number	☐ Shape	☐ Where
☐ Movement	☐ Mood	☐ Background	☐ Perspective	☐ When	☐ Sound

18

The Platypus

The furry brown platypus swam through the stream. The strange animal with a duckbill and webbed feet dove to the muddy bottom. There, the platypus used his rubbery bill to dig for worms. He put the worms in his cheek pouches. Then he swam to the surface to eat his tasty meal.

Vocabulary:

duckbill: having a rounded bill like a duck's bill
pouches: small pockets in the cheeks
webbed: having a skin that connects the toes together

---

1 **First Sentence:** The furry brown platypus swam through the stream.

What did those words make you picture? _____

_____

_____

1. What did you picture for the platypus?_____

   _____

2. What color did you picture the platypus?_____

   _____

3. What did you picture for the fur on the platypus?_____

   _____

4. What did you see for the stream?_____

   _____

---

2 **Second Sentence:** The strange animal with a duckbill and webbed feet dove to the muddy bottom.

What did those words make you picture? _____

_____

_____

1. What did you picture for the duckbill?_____

   _____

2. What did you picture for the platypus's webbed feet?_____

   _____

3. How did you see the platypus diving to the bottom?_____

   _____

4. What did you picture for the muddy bottom?_____

   _____

Third Sentence: There, the platypus used his rubbery bill to dig for worms.

What did those words make you picture? _____

_____

_____

1. What did you picture for the rubbery bill? _____

_____

2. What did you picture for the platypus digging with his bill? _____

_____

3. Where did you picture the platypus digging? _____

_____

4. What did you picture for the worms? _____

_____

Fifth Sentence: Then he swam to the surface to eat his tasty meal.

What did those words make you picture? _____

_____

_____

1. What did you see for the surface? _____

_____

2. Did you picture the platypus swimming quickly or slowly to the surface?

_____

3. What did you picture for the platypus's meal? _____

_____

Fourth Sentence: He put the worms in his cheek pouches.

What did those words make you picture? _____

_____

_____

1. What did you picture for the platypus's cheek pouches? _____

_____

2. What did you see for the platypus putting worms in his cheeks? _____

_____

3. How many worms did you picture the platypus putting in his mouth?

_____

4. What did you picture for the platypus's cheeks with the worms inside?

_____

Picture Summary:

Number your images in order.

The platypus put worms in his cheek pouches.

The platypus swam to the surface to eat.

The platypus swam through the stream and dove to the bottom.

The platypus used his rubbery bill to dig for worms.

Critical Thinking

Write a Word Summary:

_____

_____

_____

_____

_____

Main Idea:

Check the box that best describes all your images—the main idea.

☐ The platypus has a rubbery bill that he uses to dig for worms.

☐ The platypus dove to the bottom of the stream and dug a meal of worms to eat.

☐ The platypus swam to the surface to eat his tasty meal.

HOT Questions:

1. Why do you think the platypus is called a "strange animal"?_____

_____

2. Why do you think the platypus needs a bill?_____

_____

3. Why do you think the bill of a platypus is rubbery?_____

_____

4. Why might the platypus need to have webbed feet?_____

_____

5. Why do you think the platypus got the worms from the bottom of the stream and not from on land?_____

_____

6. Why might it be easier for the platypus to eat on the surface rather than under the water?_____

_____

Make up a story about Paddy the Platypus.

_____

_____

_____

_____

_____

_____

_____

_____

_____

_____

_____

_____

_____

_____

_____

_____

_____

Did you use all of the Structure Words? Check each one you used.

| ☐ What | ☐ Size | ☐ Color | ☐ Number | ☐ Shape | ☐ Where |
| ☐ Movement | ☐ Mood | ☐ Background | ☐ Perspective | ☐ When | ☐ Sound |

19

A Lake Monster?

A strange snake-like monster might live in the dark depths of Lake Okanagan. People say they have seen the huge monster swim to the surface. He sticks his head and long neck out of the water. Then he dives under the water and no one sees him again for a long time.

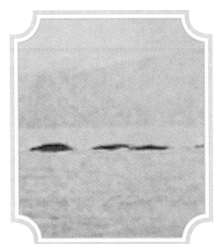

Vocabulary:

depths: the deepest parts
Lake Okanagan: a large lake in British Columbia, Canada
surface: the top or outer part

---

1 **First Sentence:** A strange snake-like monster might live in the dark depths of Lake Okanagan.

What did those words make you picture?_____

_____

_____

1. What did you picture for the the snake-like monster and what size was it?
   _____

2. What color did you picture for the monster?_____

   _____

3. Where did you picture the snake-like monster living?_____

   _____

4. What did you picture for the depths of Lake Okanagan?_____

   _____

---

2 **Second Sentence:** People say they have seen the huge monster swim to the surface.

What did those words make you picture?_____

_____

_____

1. What did you picture for the people that saw the monster? Were they on a boat, on the shore, or...?
   _____

2. Where did you picture the monster swimming?_____

   _____

3. What color did you picture the lake?_____

   _____

4. What sound did you picture the monster making on the surface of the lake?
   _____

Third Sentence: He sticks his head and long neck out of the water.

What did those words make you picture?_____

_____

1. What did you picture for his head?_____

_____

2. What did you picture for his neck? _____

_____

3. What did you picture when he stuck his head and neck out of the water?

_____

4. What did you picture the monster doing when his head was out of the water?

_____

Fourth Sentence: Then he dives under the water and no one sees him again for a long time.

What did those words make you picture?_____

_____

1. What did you picture for the monster diving?_____

_____

2. Did you picture the monster go underwater quietly or did it make a splashing sound?

_____

3. What sounds can you hear?_____

_____

4. What did you picture for "no one sees him again for a long time"? ___

_____

Picture Summary:

Number your images in order.

The monster sticks his head and neck out of the water.

People say they have seen the monster.

The monster dives back under the water.

The monster lives in the lake.

Write a Word Summary:

_____

_____

_____

_____

_____

_____

Main Idea:

Check the box that best describes all your images—the main idea.

☐ A strange monster surfaces in Lake Okanagan.

☐ The monster has a long neck and head.

☐ Some people may have seen a strange monster swimming in Lake Okanagan.

HOT Questions:

1. Why do you think the story said the monster *might* live in the lake? _____

_____

2. Why might it be important that the monster live "in the dark depths of the lake"? _____

_____

3. Why do you think it is important for the monster not to live near the shore? _____

_____

4. Why do you think the monster would sometimes swim to the surface? _____

_____

5. Why do you think the monster would dive back under the water? _____

_____

6. Do you think a monster like this really exists? Why or why not? _____

_____

7. If the monster doesn't exist, what might people have seen that made them think there was a monster? _____

_____

Make up a story about a monster.

_____

_____

_____

_____

_____

_____

_____

_____

_____

_____

_____

_____

_____

_____

_____

_____

_____

Did you use all of the Structure Words? Check each one you used.

- ☐ What
- ☐ Size
- ☐ Color
- ☐ Number
- ☐ Shape
- ☐ Where
- ☐ Movement
- ☐ Mood
- ☐ Background
- ☐ Perspective
- ☐ When
- ☐ Sound

20

Ghost Ship

A long time ago, there was a ship called the Mary Celeste that became known as a ghost ship. Captain Morehouse saw it sail back and forth in the water from his ship. Finally, some of his crew rowed to the other ship and climbed aboard. Barrels of cargo were in the hold and the ship looked normal, but no one was there. No one from the ghost ship was ever found.

Vocabulary:

cargo: goods that are carried by a boat or ship
hold: the space inside the ship where the cargo is stored

---

1 First Sentence: A long time ago, there was a ship called the Mary Celeste that became known as a ghost ship.

What did those words make you picture? _____

_____

_____

1. What did you picture for a long time ago? _____

_____

2. What size did you picture the ghost ship? _____

_____

3. What did you picture for a "ghost ship"? _____

_____

4. Where did you picture the ghost ship? _____

---

2 Second Sentence: Captain Morehouse saw it sail back and forth in the water from his ship.

What did those words make you picture? _____

_____

_____

1. What did you picture for Captain Morehouse? _____

_____

2. What did you picture for the Mary Celeste? Was it made of steel or wood? _____

3. How did you see the ship sailing back and forth? _____

_____

4. What mood did you picture for Captain Morehouse when he saw the ship?

_____

Third Sentence: Finally, some of his crew rowed to the other ship and climbed aboard.

What did those words make you picture? _____

_____

1. What did you picture for the crew? _____

_____

2. What did you picture for the crew rowing to the Mary Celeste? _____

_____

3. What did you picture for the men climbing on board? _____

_____

4. What sounds did you hear? _____

_____

Fifth Sentence: No one from the ghost ship was ever found.

What did those words make you picture? _____

_____

1. What did you see for no one on the ship? _____

_____

2. What did you see for the crew not finding anyone? _____

_____

3. What sounds did you hear on the ship? _____

_____

Fourth Sentence: Barrels of cargo were in the hold and the ship looked normal, but no one was there.

What did those words make you picture? _____

_____

1. What did you picture for the cargo? _____

_____

2. What did you picture for the barrels? _____

_____

3. What did you picture for the hold? _____

_____

4. How many people did you picture the crew seeing on the ghost ship?

_____

Picture Summary:

Number your images in order.

_____ The ship was empty of people, a ghost ship.

_____ The crew members found cargo on the ship.

_____ Crew members rowed over and boarded the ship.

_____ Captain Morehouse spotted a ship sailing back and forth.

Critical Thinking

Write a Word Summary:

_____

_____

_____

_____

Main Idea:

Check the box that best describes all your images—the main idea.

☐   A ghost ship was found floating in the sea with no one aboard.

☐   Captain Morehouse sailed his ship back and forth in the sea

☐   The crew rowed over to the Mary Celeste and found cargo.

HOT Questions:

1. Why do you think Captain Morehouse noticed the Mary Celeste?_____

_____

2. Why do you think the Mary Celeste was sailing back and forth and not in a straight line?_____

_____

3. Why do you think the captain sent his crew over to the Mary Celeste?_____

_____

4. Do you think they were surprised to find no one there? Explain. _____

_____

5. What might have made the crew believe someone had been onboard recently?_____

_____

6. What do you think happened to the captain of the Mary Celeste and his crew?_____

_____

Make up a story about what happened to the captain and crew of the Mary Celeste.

_____

_____

_____

_____

_____

_____

_____

_____

_____

_____

_____

_____

_____

_____

_____

_____

_____

Did you use all of the Structure Words? Check each one you used.

☐ What	☐ Size	☐ Color	☐ Number	☐ Shape	☐ Where
☐ Movement	☐ Mood	☐ Background	☐ Perspective	☐ When	☐ Sound

Notes

Analysis of Student Performance:

Notes

Analysis of Student Performance:

Notes

Analysis of Student Performance:

Notes

Analysis of Student Performance:

Notes

Analysis of Student Performance:

_____

_____

_____

_____

_____

_____

_____

_____

_____

_____

_____

_____

_____

_____

_____

Visualizing and Verbalizing® *Graded Workbooks* Color Coding

The colored checkers along the book's spine represent the grade level of the workbook. For example, the three green checkers indicate that the workbook is written at a third grade reading level. The colored star helps differentiate between books a, b, and c in each workbook set.